KT-375-404

Scamp

Story by Jan Weeks

Illustrated by Elise Hurst

NELSON
CENGAGE Learning®

Scamp

Text: Jan Weeks
Illustrator: Elise Hurst
Editor: Kate McGough
Designer : Goanna Graphics (Vic) Pty Ltd
Typeset in platin
Reprint: Siew Han Ong

PM Plus Chapter Books
Emerald Level 26 Set B
Washed Away
Scamp
Boys Don't Dance!
The Saddest Dog
Lights in the Mine
Butterfly Notes

Text © 2002 Cengage Learning Australia Pty Limited
Illustrations © 2002 Cengage Learning Australia Pty Limited

Copyright Notice
This Work is copyright. No part of this Work may be reproduced, stored in a retrieval system, or transmitted in any form or by any means without prior written permission of the Publisher. Except as permitted under the *Copyright Act 1968*, for example any fair dealing for the purposes of private study, research, criticism or review, subject to certain limitations. These limitations include: Restricting the copying to a maximum of one chapter or 10% of this book, whichever is greater; Providing an appropriate notice and warning with the copies of the Work disseminated; Taking all reasonable steps to limit access to these copies to people authorised to receive these copies; Ensuring you hold the appropriate Licences issued by the Copyright Agency Limited ("CAL"), supply a remuneration notice to CAL and pay any required fees.

ISBN 978 0 17 009900 4
ISBN 978 0 17 009901 1 (set)

Cengage Learning Australia
Level 7, 80 Dorcas Street
South Melbourne, Victoria Australia 3205
Phone: 1300 790 853

Cengage Learning New Zealand
Unit 4B Rosedale Office Park
331 Rosedale Road, Albany, North Shore NZ 0632
Phone: 0800 449 725

For learning solutions, visit **cengage.com.au**

Printed in China by 1010 Printing International Ltd
14 15 16 17 18 18 17 16 15

Contents

CHAPTER ONE
Tilly

School holidays are my favourite time of the year. My family and I go to our holiday house at Mermaid Point, on the south coast. Our holiday house sits high on a hill and faces the ocean.

I like Mermaid Point a lot. I go for walks along the beach and feel the salt spray on my face. At night, I listen to the waves crash against the rocks. I can't see any of Mermaid Point because I'm visually impaired. I only see shadows.

Dad tells me when he sees dolphins swimming in the ocean. One day, a fisherman caught a big fish. "It's a beauty!" I heard him cry out. Then he held it for me so that I could feel its scales. They felt really slimy! Dad said they were very shiny, too.

Our holiday house has two storeys. We live upstairs. I easily manage the stairs because they have a wooden rail, and I know exactly where to find the steps.

Behind our holiday house is a national park full of gum trees. One night, a couple of years ago, Mum saw a possum high in the trees. She prepared a dish of ripe fruit and crunchy vegetables and gave it to me.

"Put the dish on the balcony, Dylan," she said. "That possum might like some!"

She was right! Every night after that, the possum came back, waiting for food. I soon felt like she was my pet, and so I named her Tilly.

"That possum seems to know the minute we arrive!" Mum said to me the last time we were back at the holiday house. "It's as though she has a sixth sense."

Mum was right. Within minutes of arriving, Tilly climbed down the trees and onto our balcony. I heard the crackling of leaves and knew that Tilly was close by. She scampered along the top of the decking, and headed towards her dish.

"You feed her too much, Dylan!" Dad told me. "She's going to end up the size of a jumbo jet."

Tilly didn't seem to mind how much I fed her. She stayed at her dish, munching away, until she had eaten every last mouthful. Then she waited to see if I had anything else for her to eat!

Tilly wasn't afraid of me. She let me sit close to her while she fed. I think she knew that I would never hurt her.

I was glad Tilly trusted me. "You're my special friend, Tilly," I told her, softly.

CHAPTER TWO
Uncle Ray and Scamp

Tilly is scared of dogs. Mum says that if she hears one, she stands perfectly still, and waits for it to go away.

Sometimes Dad sees dead possums in the park. "If dogs are let out of their yards, they sometimes kill wildlife," he tells me.

I never used to like dogs either.

You see, a long time ago, a big dog knocked me over. I was walking and it ran right into me. I also thought all dogs were smelly and had fleas!

Mum, Dad and my teacher at school used to tell me I could have a guide dog when I got older. Guide dogs are either german shepherds, labradors or golden retrievers. They are specially trained to help people who can't see. But I didn't think I wanted one.

"They become like your eyes," my teacher once told me. "When you have a guide dog, you are more independent and are better able to take care of yourself."

My teacher didn't make me change my mind. I still didn't want a dog.

★ ★ ★

Usually, Tilly visited me by herself. But sometimes, she came with another possum that we call Elephant. We call him Elephant because he sounds like one when he walks across our roof!

Elephant wasn't as shy as Tilly. Once, when Uncle Ray stayed with us, Elephant climbed onto Uncle Ray's shoulder! Uncle Ray got a fright. I heard him give a big yell!

Before our last holiday, Uncle Ray rang Dad and asked if he could come to our holiday house when we were there. He had a couple of weeks to spare before he went overseas to work and wanted to spend the time with us.

Dad was really pleased, but I wasn't.

I loved Uncle Ray a lot. It's just that I didn't want Uncle Ray to bring his dog, Scamp. Scamp had belonged to my Aunty Pat before she died.

"Of course you can bring Scamp," I had heard Dad say to Uncle Ray, over the phone.

"Why did you tell Uncle Ray he could bring Scamp?" I asked Dad, later. "What about Tilly? She doesn't like dogs."

"Scamp will sleep in the house at night," Dad answered. "That way, he won't go anywhere near Tilly."

I hoped Dad was right.

CHAPTER THREE

Scamp Escapes!

Scamp wouldn't leave me alone! Every time I sat down, he tried to lick my hand or put his head in my lap, and expected me to pat him.

Whenever I went into the backyard, he was there, trying to get me to play with him.

"Go away!" I said and pushed Scamp away. "I don't like dogs!"

Mum tried to get me to feed Scamp but I didn't want anything to do with him.

"He's really a friendly dog," Mum said. "If you give him a chance, you might even get to like him!"

I didn't want to like him.

★ ★ ★

One night, Scamp escaped out of the house. Someone had forgotten to latch the screen door that led to the balcony. I heard Scamp out on the balcony, barking.

I panicked – Tilly was eating her dinner. But she also heard the danger, and I heard her scampering off.

"Now look what you've done!" I yelled at whoever it was who had left the door open. "The dog's out!"

I was so upset that I tripped over a chair in the lounge-room.

"There's no need for you to panic," Dad said, helping me to my feet. "Tilly's all right. I can hear her on the roof."

Scamp continued barking. I heard him run down the stairs, through the backyard and into the bush.

Uncle Ray had rushed out the screen door, onto the balcony, as soon as Scamp had escaped. I heard him calling Scamp's name, trying to get him to come back. But Scamp was gone.

"I hope he doesn't hurt Tilly!" I said, loudly.

Eventually, Scamp came home. I was in bed, but I heard Uncle Ray softly open the balcony screen door and let Scamp in. Now I disliked Scamp even more than before.

The next night, I put out lots of Tilly's favourite fruit. I even asked Mum to chop it up into little pieces in the hope that Tilly would smell it.

"Tilly!" I called.

But Tilly didn't come for her dinner.

Eventually, Dad shone a torch into the trees but there were no possums hiding in the branches.

"I hope Scamp hasn't hurt her," I said. I felt sick with worry.

CHAPTER FOUR
An Unlikely Hero

The next day, Dad's friend, Stephen, popped in to see him. His holiday house also backed onto the national park.

"That dog of yours is a hero," Stephen said to Uncle Ray.

I wondered what he meant. How could a dog that scared possums be a hero?

"Didn't you hear the fox?" Stephen asked. "It tried to break into my chicken coop. If it hadn't been for your dog, the fox would have killed my chickens."

So that explained why Scamp had been barking. He had heard the fox and had run out to scare it away. But I was still really angry, and I still didn't want to like Scamp.

★　★　★

It was really lonely at the holiday house without Tilly. I missed her company. "I wish she'd come back," I said to Mum. "I really miss her."

But Tilly didn't come back. And neither did Elephant. The only animal I had around me was Scamp.

I stood in the backyard and felt Scamp push something wet into my hand. It was his ball.

"If you throw it, Scamp will bring it back to you," said Uncle Ray, gently.

I took the ball from Scamp's mouth and threw it as hard as I could, across the yard. I heard Scamp race through the dead leaves as he chased after it.

Then I heard Scamp run back to me, and I felt the wet ball being pushed back into my hand. Scamp panted as he waited for me to throw it again.

"Good dog!" I said without thinking.

The next morning, as I ate my breakfast, Uncle Ray asked me if I wanted to take Scamp for a walk.

I wondered how he thought I could do it. Not when I couldn't see.

"All you need to do is hold onto his lead," Uncle Ray said. "I'll come with you if you like. We'll go to the shop. I want to buy a newspaper."

We went downstairs. I waited for Uncle Ray to put the lead on Scamp but, instead, he gave the lead to me.

"You can do it, Dylan," Uncle Ray told me, and put my hand on Scamp's collar. "You can feel where the lead clips onto his collar."

I was worried that Scamp would try to run away, but he didn't. He walked beside me all the way to the shop.

"Your Aunty Pat used to take Scamp for lots of walks," Uncle Ray said. "They were always together. After she died, Scamp pined for her for a long time. It's good that he's been able to make friends with you."

That night, Scamp put his furry head in my lap, and I didn't push him away.

CHAPTER FIVE
Old and New Friends

Not long after that, Uncle Ray had to leave. He had to go to catch his plane.

Before he left, Uncle Ray asked me if I wanted to look after Scamp while he was away. He said it would be for a long time.

Mum and Dad left the decision to me. They knew how I felt about dogs. But I wasn't sure how I felt. I *used* to be frightened of dogs, but Scamp had changed my feelings.

I still missed Tilly, but without Scamp I knew I would be really lonely.

"Of course I'll take care of him," I said as I patted Scamp. I was surprised at how happy I felt.

★ ★ ★

Scamp and I had to wait until the next school holidays before we went back to the holiday house. When we did, I was in for a wonderful surprise.

I was sitting inside the house with Scamp when I heard a noise. It was coming from the balcony.

At first, I thought it was Mum and Dad, but then they called out to me.

"There's someone out here who wants to see you!" they said.

I hurried out the screen door. Scamp didn't get up and follow me. He let me go by myself.

Once outside, I could barely believe what Mum told me.

"Tilly is back!" said Mum. I could tell from her voice she was smiling. "And she's brought a baby possum with her!"

"That explains why we haven't seen her," Dad said. "Tilly's been very busy becoming a mother."

"What does the baby look like?" I asked, feeling really excited. "Is it just like Tilly?"

"What we can see of it!" Dad answered.

"The baby is safe in Tilly's pouch. We can just see its little tail sticking out," Mum said and we all laughed.

Tilly never visited me after that. That was the last time. I think she came back to let me know she was safe and that she'd had a baby. Now, whenever I think of Tilly and Elephant, I think of them in the bush, high up in a tree, taking care of their family.

And I know that they are happy because that's what possums are meant to do. Dad says you can't keep wild animals as pets. They need to be free.

And that's true. But some animals are really great pets – especially Scamp.